HOME
noises

Wayne Jackman
Illustrated by
Terry McKenna

 firefly

'NYAAOW NYAAOW,' shouted Jack as he ran along the hallway, pretending to be an aeroplane. 'NYAAOW!'
'Look out!' called Mum. It was too late. CRASH! The chair fell over.

CRASH!

Just then the doorbell rang:
DING-DONG, DING-DONG.
'I'll get it!' called Jack.
CLONK went the handle as he turned it.
'BOO!' said Jack's friend, Sarah. She
had come to play at Jack's house.

It was Saturday and everyone was helping to clean the house. Dad filled a bucket with water to wash the kitchen floor.
SLIP-SLOP, SLIP-SLOP went the mop.

SLIP-SLOP

Mum put Jack's muddy tracksuit into the washing machine.
SHISH-A-SHISH-A-SHISH went the machine when she switched it on.

Jack and Sarah were playing upstairs.
'POW POW POW!' shouted Sarah as
she pretended to be a cowboy. Jack was
chasing her. He was a police car.
'DEE DA, DEE DA!' he wailed.

Suddenly another noise came from the room next door. Jack's baby brother, Matthew had woken up.
'WAAAA, WAAAAA!' he cried.

Next door, Mr Lewis and his daughter
Rosie were working in the garden.
They were mending a wooden fence that
had been blown down by the wind.
ZIG ZAG, ZIG ZAG went the saw.
BANG BANG went the hammer.

Jack and Sarah crept into the garden and popped up to surprise them. 'BLAAAH! ZAP!' they whooped, pretending they had ray guns. 'OWWW!' shouted Mr Lewis. He had hit his thumb with the hammer.

In the house, it was feeding time for the
pets. Dad opened the tins.
RUFF RUFF barked Buster the dog.
MIAAOOW! mewed Frisky the ginger
tomcat.

Buster and Frisky were very hungry.
They buried their heads in their food
bowls and munched:
CHOMP CHOMP CHOMP.
Dad gave them a saucer of milk.
SLURP SLURP SLURP they went.

CHOMP
CHOMP
CHOMP

SLURP
SLURP
SLURP

Nicky was in her bedroom. She had just
bought a new record by her favourite
pop star. She turned on the record
player at full blast.
BOOM CH-BOOM CH-CH-CH-CH
BOOM BOOM went the music.

In the room below, the phone rang:
BRRRING BRRRING.
Mum answered it, but she couldn't hear
herself talk. She picked up a broom and
banged on the ceiling:
THUMP THUMP THUMP.

Mum was lighting a fire in the sitting
room. She arranged the wood and coal
in the fireplace and then lit a match:
ZZZZIPP!
Soon the fire began to burn:
CRACKLE CRACKLE SNAP SNAP.

There was a tap at the window:
RAT-A-TAT TAT.
It was Sarah's Mum, Sue. She had come
to collect Sarah. Mum let her in and
Dad opened a bottle of wine.
POP! went the cork.

After a while, Sarah and her Mum went
home. Then Jack helped Dad to get the
supper ready.
CLUNK CLUNK CLANG went the
saucepans as Jack got them out of the
cupboard.

SIZZLE SIZZLE went the eggs in the frying pan. Then everyone sat down to eat.
CLICKETY-CLACK went their knives and forks.

SIZZLE
SIZZLE!

After supper, it was time for Jack's bath.
DRIP DRIP DRIP went the leaky tap.
Jack turned the taps on.
SLOSH SLOSH went the water as it
filled up the bath.

Jack blew bubbles in the bath water:
BUB-A-LUB, BUB-A-LUB.
Then he remembered to brush his teeth.
WOOSH-A-WOOSH went the
toothbrush as he brushed up and down.

Jack decided to have a bounce on his
bed before going to sleep.
BOING BOING squeaked the bed-
springs. Bouncing made Jack thirsty.
He went to get a drink of water.

Jack crept along the hallway:
PATTER PATTER PATTER.
Then he switched on the light in the
bathroom: CLICK.
Jack drank some water and then ran
back to bed:
PATTER PATTER PATTER BOING!

PATTER PATTER PATTER BOING!

Jack shared his bedroom with his baby brother.

'PSSST! Matthew,' he whispered. 'Are you asleep?'

'DA DA GA GA GA!' said Matthew.

Jack listened to the traffic outside:
HMMMMMM BRRMMMMM.
The clock in his room had a loud tick:
TICK TOCK, TICK TOCK.
Soon Jack was fast asleep and snoring:
ZZZZZZZZ.

Titles in this series

Farm Noises
Home Noises
Street Noises

First published in 1990 by
Firefly Books Limited
61 Western Road, Hove
East Sussex BN3 1JD

British Library Cataloguing in Publication Data
Jackman, Wayne
  Home Noises
  1. Noise
  I. Title.   II. Mckenna, Terry
  III. Series
  620.23

  ISBN 1 85485 0520

Typeset by DP Press Limited, Sevenoaks, Kent
Printed in Italy by G. Canale & C.S.p.A., Turin
Bound in Belgium by Casterman, S.A.